Egg
Fried Rice

Written by Roderick Hunt
Illustrated by Nick Schon,
based on the original characters
created by Roderick Hunt and Alex Brychta

Say the sound and read the words

igh

- br**igh**t
- l**igh**t
- r**igh**t

ie

- fr**ie**d
- tr**ie**d
- cr**ie**d

y

try

sky

cry

i–e

nice

rice

nine

"I will be nine on Friday," said
Wilma. "I'd like to eat out."

"I'd like a Chinese meal," Wilma said,
"and can we invite Biff and Chip?"

"That's fine," said Mum.

It was time for the Chinese meal.
They went to the Bright Sky.

"What is it like to be nine?" said Chip.

Wilma smiled.

"It's all right," she said.

"What do you like best?"
said Dad.

"I like egg fried rice," said Wilma,
"and I'll try tiger prawns."

Then all the lights went out.
Oh no! There was a fire.

"The kitchen is on fire!" said
Mr Lee.

They had to go outside.
Fire-fighters came to put the
fire out.

"I am sorry," said Mr Lee.

"We must shut for the night."

Wilma was upset. She tried not to, but she cried.

"It is sad to see Wilma cry," said
Mr Lee. "Come back on Sunday night."

On Sunday, Mr Lee put on
a feast.

"Smile," said Mr Lee.

"This is so kind," said Mum.

"I had my egg fried rice," said
Wilma, "and such a nice time."

Talk about the story

Word jumble

Make the *igh*, *ie*, *i–e* and *y* words from the story.

t   r   igh   b

n   e   f   i

s   igh   l   t

y   r   c

e   n   c   i

k s y

ie f d r

i c r e

c ie r d

Picture puzzle

Find as many *igh*,
ie, i–e and *y* words as
you can in the picture.

y

ie

igh

i-e

Answers: smile, egg fried rice, Chinese dragon, white, the Bight Sky restaurant

ie, i-e, y or igh?

Choose the letters to make each word.

n____t   n__n__   sm__l__

tr____d   l__k__   r____t

br____t   fr____d   cr__